4-

GRANDFATHER'S STORY

Philippa Moran.

Michael Foreman

M
Mabecron Books

First published in Great Britain in 2018 by Mabecron Books Ltd, Briston Orchard, St Mellion, Saltash, Cornwall, PL12 6RQ United Kingdom. All rights reserved.

Typeset in Sabon
Designed by Peter Bennett

10 9 8 7 6 5 4 3 2 1

ISBN 978 09955 02833

Printed and bound in Malaysia

GRANDFATHER'S

STORY

Philip Moran
illustrated by
Michael Foreman

GRANDFATHER AS A YOUNG BOY

Jack, Soggy and Grandfather looked out of the window at the rough sea and pouring rain. 'Not a good day for the beach,' said Soggy. 'What can we do instead?'

Jack had an idea ... 'Grandfather,' he said, 'Would you tell us a story about when you were a young boy? Was the world very different then?'

Grandfather laughed and said, 'It was different all right! The country - the whole world - was at war, life was much more difficult for everyone.'

'Oh it must be awful to be in a war,' said Soggy. 'Were you frightened?'

'Oh yes, I was scared all right, but it was also strangely exciting,' said Grandfather.

I was three years old when the war began, and lived in Plymouth with my younger brother and sister and our mum. Dad was away in the Army. We lived near the docks and they became an important target for the enemy bombers. There were many air-raids on the city.

One morning we came out of the air-raid shelter and saw that our house had been bombed. Our piano had blown halfway through the wall and was dangling over the street!

'That's it,' Mum said, 'Enough is enough, it is too dangerous to stay here.'

We were going to escape the city in a special train. It took us to a lovely, quiet, country area where the local police officer found us some lodgings. It was on a farm and we soon settled in and were very happy there. Our idyllic stay was very brief. The Army needed the farm and the children were all evacuated.

'What does evacuated mean?' asked Jack.

'It means,' said Grandfather, 'being moved to a place where you can stay and be safe until the war is over, but not with your parents.'

My little brother was only two and he was sent to a nursery in Devon. My sister was six and she was sent away to Somerset. Mum stayed on the farm to work and help feed the troops. Oddly enough they sent me back to St Ives, where I had been born.

'That's awful!' cried Soggy, 'You were only three and you were left all alone.'

'Ah, but I was not really alone,' said Grandfather, smiling. 'There were twenty-two of us children and we came on the train from all parts of the country.'

We had several scary moments on the train journey with enemy aircraft reported overhead. When we finally arrived at St Ives and saw the bay spread out in front of us, we all cheered 'Hooray!' We thought we would be safe at last and were ready for some exciting childhood adventures in this wonderful place.

'And it's still a wonderful place for adventures!' said Soggy.

We all climbed onto the back of a lorry, and the driver Mr Phillips drove us around town to houses where people had agreed to take in evacuees. If the lady of the house looked a bit grumpy we turned our backs or hid behind each other. But if she looked warm and friendly we shouted, 'Pick Me! Pick Me!'

'Eventually there were only two of us left on the lorry ... and then there was only one ... and can you guess who that was?'

'What!' gasped Soggy, 'Were you the only one left? Poor you, Grandfather! What happened next?'

'Well', said Grandfather, 'St Ives was like an Army Camp, full of American Marines and British Commandos and they had filled up all the spare rooms. Every bed in the town was taken.'

Mr Phillips called back to me, 'There's one more place we can try, lad. Let's go see Mrs Farnham down by the beach.'

Mrs Farnham was round and jolly and was already looking after thirteen other young boys.

'Come live with us, my lovely,' she said, 'One more won't make any difference!'

And so, at the age of three, I began my new life, settling in with the others and making the best of it.

At first, being the youngest, I was teased. They said that the red anemones on the rocks, which squirted water when you poked them with a stick, were *dead German pilots' eyeballs*. But underneath it all they were good boys, and Mrs Farnham always told us to 'look after each other and share everything.'

On Saturdays, we all lined up for a spoonful of castor oil to keep our bodies fit.

On Sundays, we went to all the different churches and chapels in town.
We judged the strength of their faith by the cakes and sandwiches we were given after the service.

At the weekends we would often hang about on the wharf, where the soldiers and local women would hold a street dance. There was always a band in the back of a jeep.

My feet were rather large for a small boy and for quite a long time I went to school in an old pair of wooden Dutch clogs. I had to move fast to stop them flying off my feet. That's when I earned my first nickname, *Horsey*, as I galloped noisily over the cobbles.

Life seemed peaceful away from the cities of war and we spent many happy hours outside, just building sandcastles on *our* beach. One day, when we were tucked in at the island end of the beach, we could hear an aeroplane coming toward us. We stood up to wave and cheer ... but as the pilot flew overhead, he started to machine-gun the beach.

We fled inside and dived under the large kitchen table.
There was a deafening explosion and it turned out that they had bombed the nearby gasworks. We all huddled together under the table loudly singing our favourite hymn, *For those in Peril on the Sea*. It helped to keep our spirits up.

'Grandfather!' exclaimed Jack, 'How could you sleep at night with all that danger around?'

'It wasn't easy, indeed some nights we could see the flashes from the convoys lighting up the horizon.'

Another dramatic time, a boy called Jimmy came rushing through the door shouting, 'Get to the harbour quick. There are fish everywhere!' We all rushed down to the harbour, tripping over the cobbles in our excitement. The tide had gone out and the pools which were left behind were filled with mackerel and sprats. Crowds of people, children and seagulls were falling over each other, all trying to catch the hundreds of mackerel which were still trying to catch the thousands of sprats!

'Wow!' said Jack. 'That sounds like much more fun!'

W̶e boys caught so many mackerel we thought we would get rich selling them around the town. But no such luck, everyone had so much fish that nobody wanted ours. The townsfolk had their share, the gulls could hardly fly and the cats could barely walk....

We made not a penny and had to throw the now curling dead fish back into the sea; our imagined riches disappearing with the tide.

'Oh, poor Grandfather,' said Jack.

'Not to worry,' replied Grandfather. 'As you know I became a fisherman and spent most of my life catching mackerel and sprats. And herring, and all the many other kinds of fish too. I never grew rich but I had a wonderful time!'

'I want to be a fisherman,' said Jack.

'And I want to sail around the world!' said Soggy.

'Perhaps we'll do it together one day,' said Grandfather.

Oh, and there was another strange day I would like to tell you about. This time the harbour was not full of fish, but was filled with a tremendous movement of people. There was a real sense of excitement in the air and we could see huge army lorries overflowing with American soldiers. We ran along the quay shouting out the time-honoured phrase, 'Give us some gum, chum!'

In reply they started throwing everything towards us - watches, cigarettes, sweets and other personal possessions. It was as if they felt they no longer needed their stuff, they were going off to war and knew they might never come back....

'So sad,' said Jack as Soggy dried a tear from his eye.

About a year before the war ended, I was told that my mum was returning to collect me! However, no one seemed to know when exactly. It seems that I was so excited I spent the next two weeks, from dawn till dusk, sitting on the corner of our street waiting for her to appear. But she did appear and then Mum, my little brother, my big sister and me all settled in a tiny cottage in the Digey.

Life was hard and money was in short supply. Mum worked in a pub serving the locals and she had another job scrubbing people's floors. But we were still happy.

One day, when I was eight years old, I stomped into our house and told Mum I really, really, needed a swimsuit. I was too grown up to swim naked any longer. Mum never argued or bothered to explain that we had no money. 'No problem,' she said, 'Wait there.' She returned from the bedroom and said, 'Wear these!'

Back at the beach I soon realised that life had not got any easier. I now stood on the edge of the water in a pair of my sister's blue school knickers!

'What!' laughed Jack, 'You had to wear your sister's knickers? How embarrassing Grandfather!'

'Yes it was,' said Grandfather, 'and when you've stopped giggling, I will tell you about our first Christmas together – the first in a very long time.'

It was Christmas Eve and we were about to hang our socks on the mantelpiece, ready for Santa's visit. Mum suddenly saw sparks caught in the chimney.

'Quick! Quick,' she cried. 'Get the fireman who lives down the road! I think the house might be about to catch fire!'

The neighbourly fireman called out the *entire* Fire Brigade *and* the big red engine. There was so much excitement in our tiny street as they dealt with, what turned out to be, a very small chimney fire.

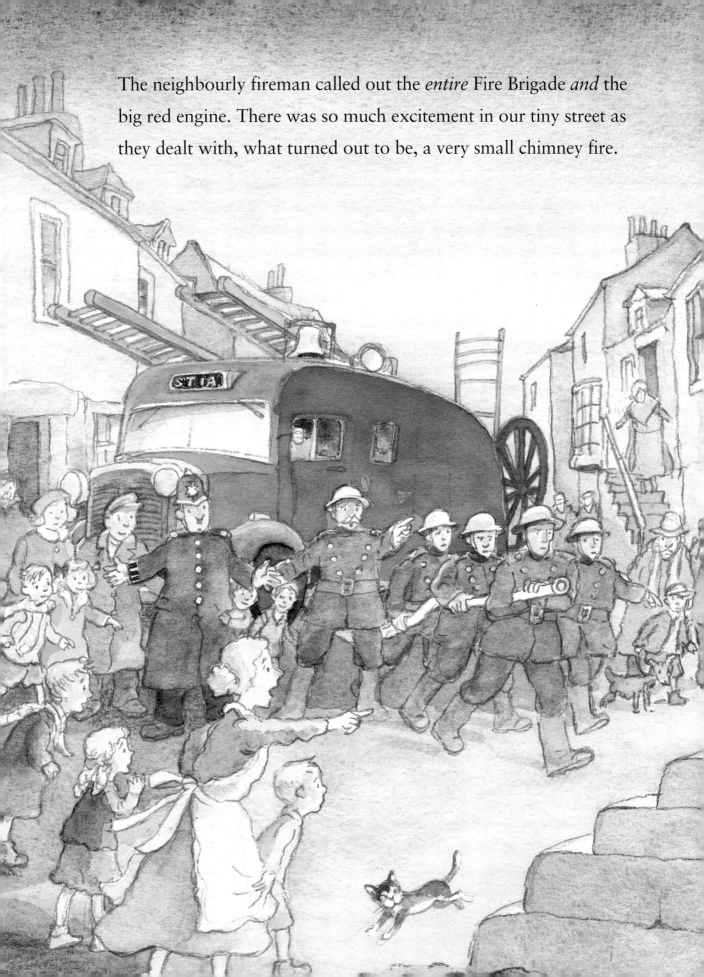

The next morning, having hung our socks up on the mantelpiece after the firemen left, we rushed down to find our presents. We all had an orange and a tin of Horlicks tablets, as there were no sweets available then.

And what a great day it was. We were together, the war was over, and it was the best Christmas ever!

'Oh, good!' cheered Jack, 'A happy ending!'

'Not only that,' said Soggy, 'Look! The sun's coming out....'

'Let's all go to the beach!'